D0510367

A seal pup was on the sand.
"It has no mother!" said Chip.

"Perhaps the mother is getting food," said Mum.

"But what if the pup is lost?"
asked Biff.

"Let's wait to see if the mother comes back," said Dad.

But the mother did not come back.
So, in the end, Dad sent for help.

At last the Seal Rescue Team came.
Mrs Hill looked at the seal pup.

"We must get him into the boat,"
she said.

Mrs Hill and her team got the
seal pup into the boat.

"He is not well," said Mrs Hill.
"He needs food."

The children went to see the seal.
They called him Sinbad.

"He is a lot better," said Mrs Hill.
"I am glad you called us."

The children went back to see
Sinbad. He was big and fit.

"Now he can go back in the sea,"
said Mrs Hill.

"We can let him go at last,"
said Mrs Hill.

They took the seal out in a boat.
Sinbad went in with a splash!

"Look at Sinbad," said Kipper.
"He's saying goodbye!"